Life
CHANGER

A GRAPHIC GUIDE TO THE LIFE OF JESUS

MOST OF US WOULD LIKE TO CHANGE OUR LIFE IN SOME WAY.

SOME OF US WONDER WHAT GOD THINKS OF OUR LIFE.

THIS BOOK IS ABOUT A LIFE WHICH TRANSFORMED THE WORLD AND THE FUTURE. IT'S ABOUT A LIFE CHANGER...

SYMBOLS USED IN THIS BOOK

 I LOVE YOU

 TURN AROUND TO LIVE WITH GOD AS KING

 YES/AGREE/ APPROVE

 BAD ACTIONS/ ATTITUDE/THOUGHTS

 NO/DISAPPROVE/ REJECT

 GOOD ACTIONS/ ATTITUDE/THOUGHTS

 GOD THE KING

 GOD THE KING DIED AND ROSE AGAIN

 CHANGED. A NEW HEART WHERE GOD IS KING

1. life begins

MARY AND JOSEPH WERE IN LOVE,
AND ENGAGED TO BE MARRIED.

AN ANGEL BROUGHT NEWS THAT MARY WAS CHOSEN TO BRING THE KING, GOD'S SON, INTO THE WORLD.

READ THE FULL STORY IN LUKE 1 V 26-38.

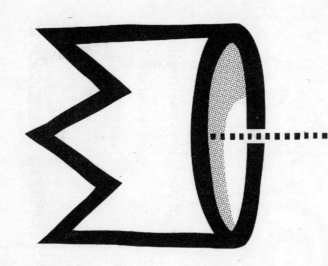

THE GOD WHO MADE ALL THINGS ENTERED OUR WORLD AS ONE OF US. AS A BABY.

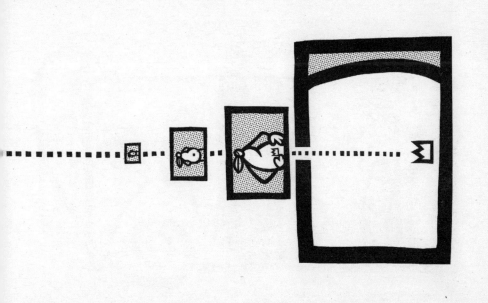

WHEN JOSEPH FOUND OUT MARY WAS PREGNANT,
HE DECIDED TO END THINGS.

BUT AN ANGEL TOLD HIM THE FULL STORY.
SO HE CHANGED HIS MIND.

READ THE FULL STORY
IN MATTHEW 1 V 18-24.

SUDDENLY, SOME ANGELS APPEARED. THEY ANNOUNCED
THE ARRIVAL OF THE KING.

MARY AND JOSEPH CALLED THE BABY
JESUS. AND HE GREW INTO A MAN...

2. who is Jesus?

JESUS' COUSIN, JOHN, WAS A MESSENGER FROM GOD. HE TOLD PEOPLE TO GET READY FOR GOD'S ARRIVAL.

HE TOLD THEM TO STOP IGNORING GOD, AND TO CHANGE HOW THEY LIVED. HE SAID THEY NEEDED TO START TREATING GOD AS THEIR KING.

READ THE FULL STORY IN MARK 1 V 4-8.

JOHN KNEW WHO JESUS WAS.

JOHN BAPTISED JESUS. WHILE JESUS WAS IN THE WATER, HIS FATHER GOD SPOKE TO HIM. HE SAID: "YOU ARE MY SON. I LOVE YOU. I AM PLEASED WITH YOU."

YOU CAN READ ABOUT THIS IN MARK 1 V 9-11.

3. jesus v the devil

AFTER JESUS HAD BEEN BAPTISED,
HE WENT INTO THE DESERT TO FACE
THE DEVIL.

THE DEVIL WANTED TO CORRUPT GOD'S SON. SO HE
QUESTIONED WHETHER JESUS WAS REALLY THE KING.

THE DEVIL OFFERED JESUS POWER OVER THE
WHOLE WORLD, IF JESUS WOULD FOLLOW HIM.

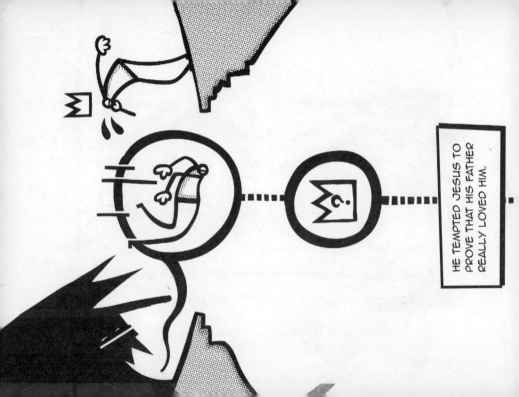

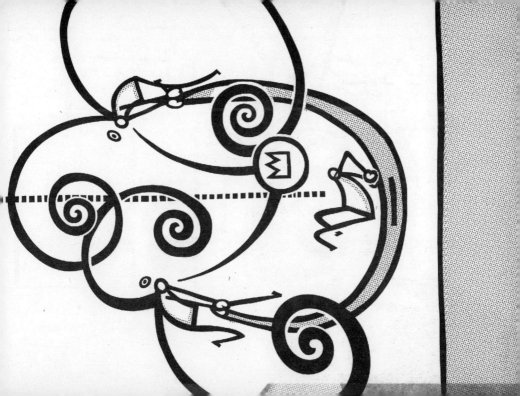

BUT JESUS PUT HIS FOOT DOWN. HE TOLD THE DEVIL: NO!

4. jesus v the storm

JESUS CALLED A MIXTURE OF PEOPLE TO JOIN HIM, CALLED HIS DISCIPLES. THEY KNEW JESUS WAS SPECIAL...

BUT NOT *HOW* SPECIAL.

THEN ONE DAY, JESUS WAS CROSSING
A SEA WITH HIS FOLLOWERS.

THERE WAS A SUDDEN,
TERRIFYING STORM.

JESUS' FRIENDS THOUGHT THEY
WERE GOING TO DIE.

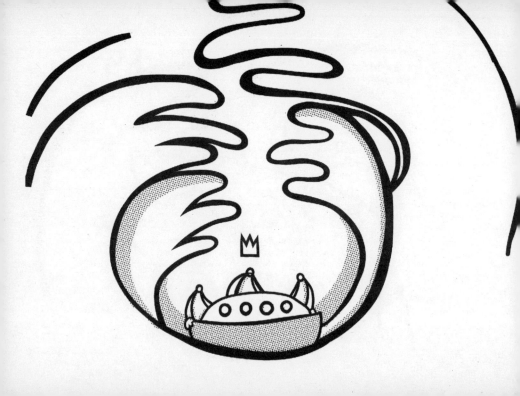

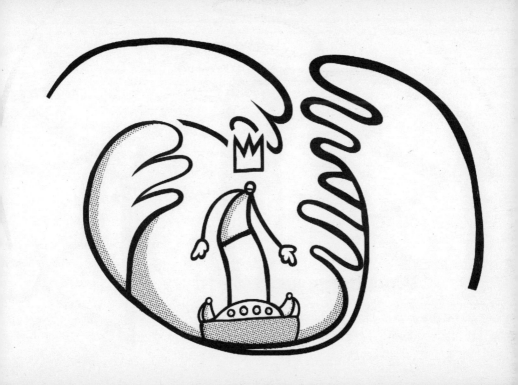

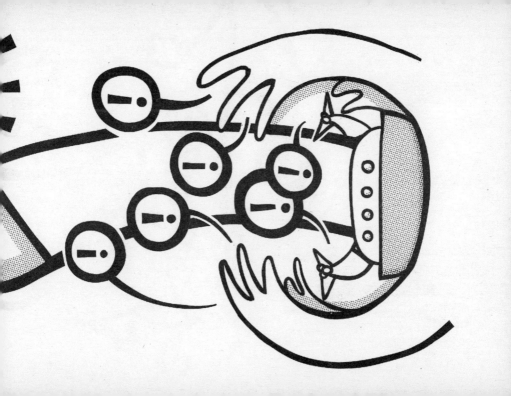

THE SEA WAS CALM.
THE DISCIPLES ASKED:
"WHO IS THIS...?"

"EVEN THE WIND AND THE WAVES OBEY HIM!"

READ THE FULL STORY
IN MARK 4 V 35-41.

5. jesus v the religious guys

THE RELIGIOUS LEADERS SAID THEY
LOVED GOD AS THEIR KING.

THEY GOT ANGRY AND TOLD JESUS HE WAS
WRONG. THEY POINTED OUT THAT THEY HAD DONE
LOADS OF GOOD THINGS.

JESUS TOLD THEM TO LOOK AT THEIR HEARTS.

HE EXPLAINED THAT EVERY HEART HAS A TERRIBLE PROBLEM.

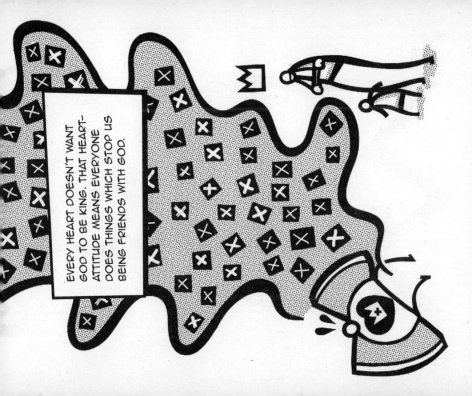

EVERY HEART DOESN'T WANT GOD TO BE KING. THAT HEART-ATTITUDE MEANS EVERYONE DOES THINGS WHICH STOP US BEING FRIENDS WITH GOD.

READ ABOUT SOME OF THOSE THINGS IN MARK 7 V 14-23

JESUS SAID THAT IF THESE ACTIONS, AND THE HEART-ATTITUDE WHICH CAUSES THEM, AREN'T DEALT WITH, WE CAN'T LIVE WITH GOD WHEN WE DIE. WE FACE FOR EVER SEPARATED FROM GOD AND EVERYTHING GOOD.

YOU CAN READ ABOUT WHERE PEOPLE GO WHEN THEY DIE IN LUKE 16 V 19-26.

JESUS SAID THAT EVERYONE, EVEN THE RELIGIOUS LEADERS, NEEDS TO HAVE THEIR HEARTS CHANGED SO THAT THEY CAN BE FRIENDS WITH GOD.

THE LEADERS DIDN'T LIKE THIS. THEY DIDN'T WANT TO LISTEN
TO JESUS. SO THEY DECIDED TO GET RID OF HIM.

6. "life for a failure

WHEN JESUS CAME TO TOWN, HE CLIMBED A TREE TO SEE HIM.

JESUS WANTED TO TALK
TO ZACCHAEUS.

HE WANTED TO EAT WITH ZACCHAEUS. EVERYONE WAS AMAZED.

READ THE FULL
STORY IN LUKE
19 V 1-10.

AFTER JESUS HAD WELCOMED HIM LIKE THIS, ZACCHAEUS
WANTED TO CHANGE HIS WAYS AND LIVE WITH GOD AS HIS KING.

JESUS TOLD EVERYONE THAT
HE HAD COME TO MAKE PEOPLE
ACCEPTABLE TO GOD BY DEALING
WITH THEIR HEART PROBLEM AND
ALL THE THINGS WHICH BLOCKED
ZACCHAEUS, AND US, FROM GOD.

BUT HOW WOULD HE DO IT?

7. death for a king

ONE DAY, JESUS ASKED ONE OF HIS DISCIPLES, PETER, WHO HE THOUGHT JESUS REALLY WAS.

PETER GOT IT RIGHT: JESUS IS THE KING. THEN JESUS SHOCKED
HIM BY SAYING HIS PLAN WAS TO DIE ON A CROSS.

HE TOLD JESUS HE WOULDN'T BE EXECUTED. JESUS HIT BACK HARDER. HE SAID THAT AS THE KING, HE *MUST* DIE ON A CROSS.

HAVE A READ OF JESUS' WORDS IN JOHN 3 V 16.

JUDAS WAS ONE OF
JESUS' DISCIPLES.
THE DEVIL TEMPTED HIM
TO TURN ON JESUS.

JUDAS WAS WELL PAID FOR BETRAYING JESUS. BUT THEN HE REALISED WHAT HE'D DONE...

READ THE FULL STORY
IN MATTHEW 27 V 3–5.

JESUS WAS BROUGHT TO
THE ROMAN GOVERNOR,
PONTIUS PILATE.

BECAUSE JESUS HADN'T EVER DONE ANYTHING WRONG, THE
RELIGIOUS LEADERS STRUGGLED TO GET HIM FOUND GUILTY.

PILATE HANDED JESUS OVER TO HIS MEN TO TORTURE HIM.

THEN HE GAVE THE
PEOPLE A CHOICE:
CRUCIFY JESUS OR LET HIM GO? THEY ALL SAID ONE THING...

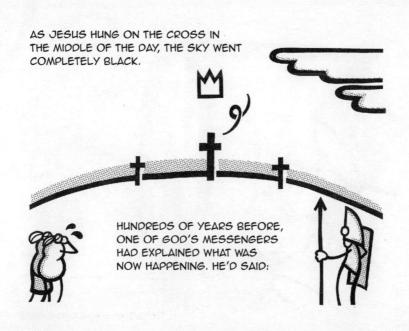

"IT WAS OUR PAINS HE COVERED - ALL THE THINGS WRONG WITH US."

"WE'VE ALL DONE OUR OWN THING, GONE OUR OWN WAY."

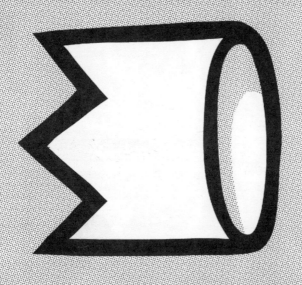

"HE TOOK THE PUNISHMENT. HE DIED."

THE RELIGIOUS LEADERS PUT SOLDIERS IN FRONT OF HIS TOMB SO THAT JESUS' BODY COULDN'T BE STOLEN.

BUT ON THE THIRD DAY AFTER JESUS DIED,
THE GROUND STARTED TO SHAKE...

READ THE FULL STORY
IN LUKE 24 V 1-8.

SOME WOMEN CAME TO SEE THE BODY. BUT ALL THEY
FOUND WAS ANGELS AND AN EMPTY TOMB!

READ THE FULL STORY
IN MATTHEW 28 V 8-10.

THEY RUSHED OFF TO TELL THE DISCIPLES. AND ON THE WAY,
THEY MET JESUS! THEY BOWED TO THEIR KING.

JESUS' DISCIPLES DIDN'T BELIEVE THE
WOMEN'S STORY. IT WAS CRAZY!

READ THE FULL STORY
IN LUKE 24 V 9-12.

READ THE FULL STORY
IN LUKE 24 V 36-44
AND JOHN 20 V 24-28.

BUT THEN JESUS APPEARED TO THEM AND PROVED
BEYOND DOUBT THAT HE REALLY WAS ALIVE.

1º. a life-changing message

THE RISEN JESUS TOLD HIS FOLLOWERS THAT
HE HAD DEALT WITH ALL THE WRONG THINGS THEY
HAD DONE, AND THAT THEY COULD LIVE WITH GOD
FOR EVER.

AND HE TOLD THEM THEY WOULD BE GIVEN NEW
HEARTS BY HIS HOLY SPIRIT.

READ THE FULL STORY IN LUKE
24 V 46-49 AND JOHN 14 V 26-27.

HE ALSO COMMANDED THEM TO GO ALL OVER THE WORLD, TELLING
PEOPLE HOW THEY COULD HAVE PERFECT LIFE WITH GOD FOR EVER.

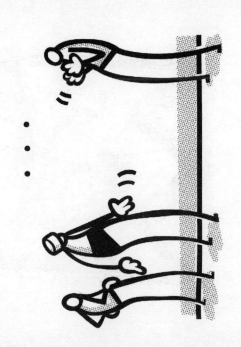

EVER SINCE THEN, JESUS' HOLY SPIRIT HAS HELPED HIS FOLLOWERS TELL OTHER PEOPLE THAT, BECAUSE KING JESUS DIED AND CAME BACK TO LIFE, THEY CAN ENJOY PERFECT LIFE WITH GOD FOR EVER, INSTEAD OF FACING FOR EVER WITHOUT GOD'S ACCEPTANCE, AND WITHOUT ANYTHING GOOD.

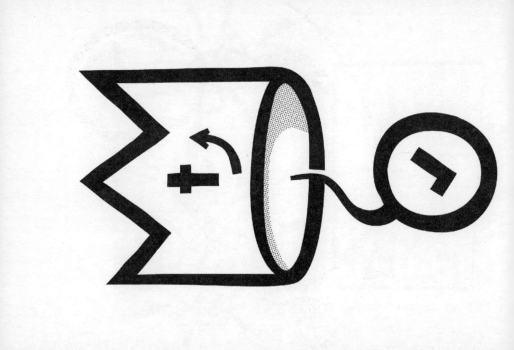

ONE OF THOSE FOLLOWERS DREW THESE PICTURES, SO THAT YOU'D HEAR THAT GREAT MESSAGE. PERHAPS ONE OF THOSE FOLLOWERS GAVE YOU THIS BOOK.

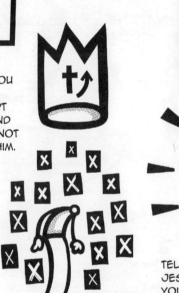

TURN BACK TO LIVING YOUR LIFE WITH JESUS IN CHARGE.

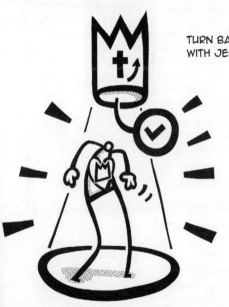

IF YOU'VE DONE THIS, YOU CAN KNOW THAT YOU HAVE A NEW HEART, AND THAT YOU'LL LIVE WITH GOD FOR EVER.

JESUS HAS CHANGED YOUR LIFE AND YOUR FUTURE!

THIS PROJECT WOULD NEVER HAVE SEEN THE LIGHT OF DAY WITHOUT THE ENCOURAGEMENT AND SUPPORT OF: TONY WAGHORN, MIKE TINDALL, DAVID FIELD, MARSH MOYLE, KEVIN CUNNINGHAM, MARK MEYNELL, DAVID BUTLER, TIM NEALE, ANDY WYATT, CONTAGIOUS, THE SIGGS & DAVE'S COMICS. THANK YOU.

THANKS ALSO TO THE GUYS AT THE GOOD BOOK COMPANY WHO WORKED SO HARD AT HONING THIS - ESPECIALLY CARL AND ANDRÉ.

AND TO FIONA, MY BEST HALF, THE ONE WITH THAT KILLER COMBINATION OF BEING BOTH BRUTAL AND BEAUTIFUL.

ABOUT THE AUTHOR

JASON RAMASAMI IS A SCHOOL TEACHER AND ILLUSTRATOR. HE ENJOYS EXPLORING WORLDVIEWS AND ENCOURAGING OTHERS TO DO THE SAME.